4-Chord Songbook

Favourite Hits

WISE PUBLICATIONS
part of The Music Sales Group

London / New York / Paris / Sydney / Copenhagen / Berlin / Madrid / Tokyo

This *4-Chord Songbook* allows even beginner guitarists to play and enjoy your favourite hits. The songs have been specially arranged so that only 4 chords are needed to play all of the songs in the book.

The *4-Chord Songbook* doesn't use music notation. Throughout the book chord boxes are printed at the head of each song; the chord changes are shown above the lyrics. It's left to you, the guitarist, to decide on a strum pattern or picking pattern.

Some of the arrangements indicate that a capo should be used at a particular fret. This is to match the song to the key of the original recording so that you can play along; otherwise the capo is not needed for playing on your own. However, if the pitch of the vocal line is not comfortable for singing (if it is pitched too high or too low) you may wish to use a capo anyway; placing the capo behind a suitable fret will change the key of the song without learning any new chords.

Whatever you do, this *4-Chord Songbook* guarantees hours of enjoyment for guitarists of all levels, as well as providing a fine basis for building a strong repertoire.

Published by
Wise Publications
14-15 Berners Street, London W1T 3LJ, UK.

Exclusive Distributors:
Music Sales Limited
Distribution Centre, Newmarket Road, Bury St Edmunds, Suffolk IP33 3YB, UK.
Music Sales Pty Limited
120 Rothschild Avenue, Rosebery, NSW 2018, Australia.

Order No. AM993102
ISBN 978-1-84772-499-1
This book © Copyright 2007 Wise Publications,
a division of Music Sales Limited.

Printed in the EU.

www.musicsales.com

Your Guarantee of Quality

As publishers, we strive to produce every book to the highest commercial standards.

The music has been freshly engraved and the book has been carefully designed to minimise awkward page turns and to make playing from it a real pleasure.

Particular care has been given to specifying acid-free, neutral-sized paper made from pulps which have not been elemental chlorine bleached.

This pulp is from farmed sustainable forests and was produced with special regard for the environment.

Throughout, the printing and binding have been planned to ensure a sturdy, attractive publication which should give years of enjoyment.

If your copy fails to meet our high standards, please inform us and we will gladly replace it.

All The Small Things
Blink 182
page 4

Baba O'Riley
The Who
page 6

Bohemian Like You
The Dandy Warhols
page 8

Common People
Pulp
page 11

Doll Parts
Hole
page 14

I Fought The Law
The Clash
page 16

I'll Be Your Baby Tonight
Bob Dylan
page 18

In The City
Razorlight
page 20

Jack And Diane
John Cougar Mellencamp
page 24

Life Of Riley
The Lightning Seeds
page 27

Mull Of Kintyre
Paul McCartney
page 30

My Best Friend's Girl
The Cars
page 32

Pain Killer (Summer Rain)
Turin Brakes
page 38

Praise You
Fatboy Slim
page 35

Rocks
Primal Scream
page 42

She Belongs To Me
Bob Dylan
page 40

Tiger Feet
Mud
page 45

Playing Guide
page 48

All The Small Things

Words & Music by
Mark Hoppus & Thomas Delonge

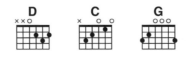

Capo 5th fret

Intro   D C ‖: G | G | D | D   C   :‖

Verse 1
```
G          D              C
All the   small things,
          D              G
True care, truth brings.
          D         C
I'll take   one lift,
          D
Your ride, best trip.
G          D        C
Always    I know
          D                G
You'll be   at my show
          D        C        D
Watching,   waiting,   com - miserating.
G                        (D)
Say it ain't so, I will not go,
          (C)
Turn the lights off, carry me (home.)
```

Chorus 1
```
G
Na, na, na, na, na na, na na na na.
home.
D                C
Na, na, na, na, na na, na na na na.
G
Na, na, na, na, na na, na na na na.
D                C
Na, na, na, na, na na, na na na na.
```

Link 1   ‖: G | G | D | D   C   :‖

Verse 2

    G   **D**   **C**
    Late night, come home,

            D   **G**
Work sucks, I know.

            D   **C**
She left me roses by the stairs,

       D   **G**
Sur - prises let me know she cares.___

               (D)
Say it ain't so, I will not go,

           (C)
Turn the lights off, carry me (home.)

Chorus 2

G
Na, na, na, na, na na, na na na na.
home.

D   **C**
Na, na, na, na, na na, na na na na.

G
Na, na, na, na, na na, na na na na.

D   **C**
Na, na, na, na, na na, na na na na.

Link 2   ‖: **G** | **G** | **C** | **D** :‖ *Play 4 times*

Coda

    G   **D**
    Say it ain't so, I will not go,

           C   **G**
Turn the lights off, carry me home.

                      D
Keep your head still, I'll be your thrill,

              C   **G**
The night will go on, my little wind - mill.

                D
Say it ain't so, I will not go,

           C   **G**
Turn the lights off, carry me home.

                      D
Keep your head still, I'll be your thrill,

              C   **G**
The night will go on, the night will go on, my little wind - mill.

5

Baba O'Riley

Words & Music by
Pete Townshend

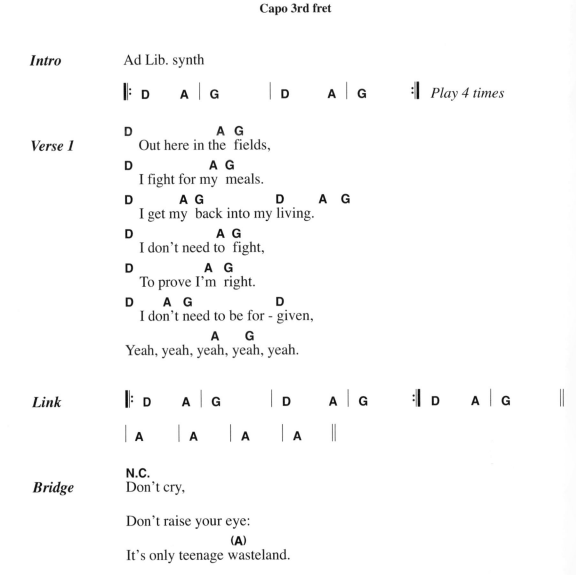

Capo 3rd fret

Intro

Ad Lib. synth

‖: D   A | G | D   A | G   :‖ *Play 4 times*

Verse 1

D   A G
Out here in the fields,

D   A G
I fight for my meals.

D   A G   D   A   G
I get my back into my living.

D   A G
I don't need to fight,

D   A G
To prove I'm right.

D   A G   D
I don't need to be for - given,

             A   G
Yeah, yeah, yeah, yeah, yeah.

Link

‖: D   A | G | D   A | G   :‖ D   A | G   ‖

| A | A | A | A   ‖

Bridge

N.C.
Don't cry,

Don't raise your eye:

                 (A)
It's only teenage wasteland.

Verse 2

```
D              A   G
  Sally, take my  hand,
D                      A   G
  We'll travel south cross land.
D              A
Put out the fire,
      G                    D       A   G
And don't look past my shoulder.
D              A   G
  The exodus is  here,
D                    A   G
  The happy ones are  near.
D                  A
Let's get together,
      G                  D     A   G
Be - fore we get much older.
```

Solo 1   ‖ D   A │ G   A │ D   A │ G   ‖

Chorus

```
              D       A   G
  Teenage wasteland,
                A   D         A   G
  It's only teen - age wasteland.
          A   D
  Teen - age wasteland,
A     G
Oh yeah,
          A   D        A   G
  Teen - age wasteland.
              A       │ A    │ G    │ G      ‖
  They're all wasted!
```

Solo 2   ‖: A   │ G   │ D   │ C   :‖

          │ D   │ D   │ C   │ C   ‖

Violin solo   │ D   (ad lib. for 36 bars)   ‖

Outro   │ A   │ A   │ A   │ A   │ D   ‖

Bohemian Like You

Words & Music by
Courtney Taylor-Taylor

Capo 2nd fret

Intro ‖: (A) | (C) | (G) | (D) :‖

‖: A | C | G | D :‖

| A D | A D | A D ‖

Verse 1

   A   D   A
    You've got a great car,
           C
Yeah, what's wrong with it today?
    G
I used to have one too,
          D
Maybe I'll come and have a look.
        A   C
I really love your hairdo, yeah,
      G
I'm glad you like mine too.
         D
See, we're looking pretty cool.

Getcha.

Link 1 | A D | A D | A D ‖

Verse 2

    A   D   A
    So what do you do?

          C
Oh yeah, I wait tables too.

      G
No, I haven't heard your band,

          D
'Cause you guys are pretty new.

         A   C
But if you dig on vegan food,

        G
Well, come over to my work,

          D
I'll have them cook you something

        A
That you really love.

Chorus 1

        C   G
'Cause I like you, yeah I like you,

        D   A
And I'm feeling so bohemian like you.

        C   G
Yeah I like you, yeah I like you,

        D
And I feel wa-ho, whoo!

Link 2

‖: A | C | G | D   :‖
                     Ooh, ooh, oooh.   Ooh, ooh, oooh.

| A   D | A   D | A   D | A   ‖
                                Wait!

Verse 3

N.C.   A   C
Who's that guy just hanging at your pad?

        G
He's looking kind of bummed.

          D
Yeah, you broke up? That's too bad.

         A   C
I guess it's fair if he always pays the rent,

        G
And he doesn't get bent about

D   A
Sleeping on the couch when I'm there.

Chorus 2

          C   G
'Cause I like you, yeah I like you,

            D   A
And I'm feeling so bohemian like you.

          C   G
Yeah I like you, yeah I like you,

            D
And I feel wa-ho, whoo!

Link 3   ‖: A | C | G | D   :‖

                          Ooh, ooh, oooh.   Ooh, ooh, oooh.

Chorus 3

          A
And I'm getting wise,

          C   G
And I feel so bohemian like you.

          D
It's you that I want,

          A   C   G
So please, just a casual, casual easy thing.

 D   A
Is it? It is for me.

          C   G   D
And I like you, yeah I like you, and I like you, I like you,

          A   C   G
I like you, I like you, I like you, I like you, I like you,

            D
And I feel who-hoa, whoo!

Coda   ‖: A | C | G | D   :‖

                          Ooh, ooh, oooh.   Ooh, ooh, oooh.

         | A   D | A   D | A   D | A   D | A   ‖

Common People

Words by Jarvis Cocker
Music by Jarvis Cocker, Nick Banks, Russell Senior,
Candida Doyle & Stephen Mackey

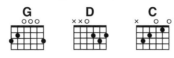

Capo 5th fret

Intro | G | G | G | G ‖

Verse 1

G
She came from Greece, she had a thirst for knowledge,

She studied sculpture at St. Martin's college,

D
That's where I caught her eye.

G
She told me that her dad was loaded,

I said "In that case I'll have rum and Coca Cola,"

D
She said "Fine."

And then in thirty seconds time she said:

Chorus 1

C
"I want to live like common people,

G
I want to do whatever common people do,

Want to sleep with common people,

D
I want to sleep with common people like you."

Well, what else could I do?

G
I said, "I'll - I'll see what I can do."

Verse 2

(G)
I took her to a supermarket,

D
I don't know why but I had to start it some - where, so it started there.

G
I said "Pretend you've got no money,"

cont.

                                                                                                   D

She just laughed and said "Oh, you're so funny," I said "Yeah?

Well I can't see anyone else smiling in here, are you sure?

Chorus 2

  C

You want to live like common people,

                                   G

You want to see whatever common people see,

You want to sleep with common people,

                                 D

You want to sleep with common people like me?"

                                         G

But she didn't understand, she just smiled and held my hand.

Bridge 1

(G)

Rent a flat above a shop, cut your hair and get a job,

                D

Smoke some fags and play some pool, pretend you never went to school,

                G

But still you'll never get it right 'cause when you're laid in bed at night

                D

Watching 'roaches climb the wall,

If you called your dad he could stop it all, yeah.

Chorus 3

  C

You'll never live like common people,

                                   G

You'll never do whatever common people do.

You'll never fail like common people,

                              D

You'll never watch your life slide out of view,

And then dance and drink and screw,

                         G

Because there's nothing else to do.

Instrumental

‖: G | G | G | G |

| D | D | D | D   :‖

12

Chorus 4

      C
    Sing along with the common people,

                                   G
Sing along and it might just get you through.

Laugh along with the common people,

                                    D
Laugh along even though they're laughing at you,

And the stupid things that you do,

                   G
Because you think that poor is cool.

Verse 3

Like a dog lying in the corner,

They will bite you and never warn you,

  D
Look out, they'll tear your insides out,

G
  'Cause everybody hates a tourist,

                               D
Especially one who thinks it's all such a laugh,

And the chip stains and grease will come out in the bath.

       C
You will never understand how it feels to live your life

       G
With no meaning or control and with nowhere left to go.

       D
You are amazed that they exist,

                                G
And they burn so bright whilst you can only wonder why.

Bridge 2   As Bridge 1

Chorus 5   As Chorus 3

Outro | **G** | **G** | **G** | **G** ||

           (G)
||: Want to live with common people like you. :|| *Play 7 times*

||: Oh, la, la, la, la. :|| *Play 4 times*

Oh yeah.

Doll Parts

Words & Music by
Courtney Love

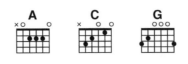

Verse 1

  A   **C**
I am doll eyes,

G   **C**
Doll mouth, doll legs.

  A   **C**
I am doll arms,

G   **C**
Big veins, dog beg.

Pre-chorus 1

 A   **C**
Yeah, they really want you,

       G   **C**
They really want you, they really do.

 A   **C**
Yeah, they really want you,

       G   **C**
They really want you, but I do too.

Chorus 1

A   **C**   **G** **N.C.**   **G**
I want to be the girl with the most cake.

A   **C**   **G**   **N.C.**   **G**
I love him so much it just turns to hate. _____

A   **C** **G** **N.C.**   **G**
I fake it so real, I am beyond fake.

  A   **C**   **G** **N.C.**   **G**
‖: And some - day you will ache like I ache. :‖ *Play 4 times*

A   **C** **G** **N.C.**
Some - day, you will ache like I ache.

Verse 2
```
     A     C
     I am  doll parts,
   G          C
   Bad skin,  doll heart.
   A          C
   It stands  for knife,
   G            C
   For the rest  of my life.
```

Pre-chorus 2
```
   A                      C
   Yeah, they really want you,
              G                C
   They really want you, they really do.
   A                    C
   Yeah, they really want you,
            G              C
   They really want you, but I do too.
```

Chorus 2
```
   A            C    G   N.C.                G
   I want to be the girl with the most cake. ____
   A        C       G
   He only loves those things,
   N.C.                              G
   Because he loves to see them break. ____
   A       C   G   N.C.               G
   I fake it so real, I am beyond fake. ____
       A       C   G   N.C.               G
   And some - day, you will ache like I ache. ____
   ‖:  A       C   G
       Some - day you will ache like I ache. :‖  *Play 6 times*
   A       C   G
   Some - day, you will ache like I ache.
```

I Fought The Law

Words & Music by
Sonny Curtis

Capo 7th fret

Intro ‖: G | C D | G | D C G :‖

Verse 1
(G)   C   G
Breakin' rocks in the   hot sun,
                              D   G
I fought the law and the   law won,
                              D   G
I fought the law and the   law won.
                              C   G
I needed money 'cause I   had none,
                              D   G
I fought the law and the   law won,
                              D   G
I fought the law and the   law won.

Chorus 1
    C
I left my baby and it feels so bad,
    G
I guess my race is run.
C
She's the best girl that I ever had,
G   D   G
I fought the law and the   law won,
                              D   C   G
I fought the law and the…

Instrumental ‖: C | C | G | G :‖ *Play 3 times*

| C | C | G | D G | G | D C G |

Verse 2

G   N.C.
Robbin' people with a   six-gun,

G   D   G
I fought the law and the   law won,

                     D   G
I fought the law and the   law won.

                  C   G
I lost my girl and I   lost my fun,

                     D   G
I fought the law and the   law won,

                     D   G
I fought the law and the   law won.

Chorus 2

      C
I left my baby and it feels so bad,

      G
I guess my race is run.

      C
She's the best girl that I ever had,

G   D   G
I fought the law and the   law won,

                     D   C   G
I fought the law and the…

Link   ‖: G | C   D | G | D C G :‖

Outro chorus

G   N.C.
I fought the law and the   law won,

I fought the law and the   law won,

I fought the law and the   law won,

I fought the law and the   law won,

(G)   (D)   (G)
I fought the law and the   law won,

(G)   (D)   (G)
I fought the law and the   law won,

(G)   (D)   (G)
I fought the law and the   law won,

(G)   D C G
I fought the law and the…

I'll Be Your Baby Tonight

Words & Music by
Bob Dylan

Tune guitar down by a tone

Intro | G | G | A | A |

| C | D | G | G ||

Verse 1
(G)
Close your eyes,

Close the door,

You don't have

   A
To worry any more.

C   **D**   **G**   **D**
  I'll be your ____ baby to - night.

Verse 2
         G
Shut the light,

Shut the shade,

       A
You don't have

To be afraid.

C   **D**   **G**
  I'll be your ____ baby to - night.

Bridge

            C

Well, that mockingbird's

Gonna sail away,

G

  We're gonna forget it.

    A

That big, fat moon

Is gonna shine like a spoon,

       D **N.C.**

But   we're gonna let it,

You won't regret it.

           G

Verse 3   Kick your shoes off,

Do not fear,

          A

Bring that bottle

Over here.

C   **D**   **G**

  I'll be your ___ baby to - night.

Outro   ‖: G | G | A | A |

           | C | D | G | G   :‖ *Repeat to fade*

In The City

Words & Music by
Johnny Borrell & John Fortis

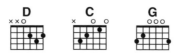

Capo 2nd fret

Intro | D C | D C G| D C | D C G ‖

Verse 1

    D   **C**
Well it's a close one, a real close one,

    D   **C**   **G**
But no-one gets hurt and she's got twice the fun,

    D   **C**
Now they kiss in the rain.

         D   **C**
And did someone call out someone's name,

       G   **D**
From a white cadillac on a white wind,

    C   **D**
To a white dress across the great divide,

         C   **G**
Into the warm moon - light?

   D   **C**
And she's been reading Bu - kowski for days,

   D   **C**   **G**
Leans over, spits her name in my face and says:

  D   **C**
"Well now you know how it feels."

  D   **C**   **G**   **D**
"Well now you know how it feels."

Chorus 1

N.C.   **D**   **C**
And I was looking for you,

D   **C** **G**
Looking for you,

D   **C**   **D**
Looking for you in the city last night.

Verse 2

        D   **C**
And the boys in the band steal a kiss,

             D
From the mystery of the night,

   C   **G**   **D**   **C**
11:59 to zero, little blonde hair and jeans, holds it tight.

             D   **C**   **G**   **D**
Turns on the heat and starts to fight and sayin': "That's my man."

                      C
Well the myth of love must have been there,

        D   **C**   **G**
The spirit of possession was there.

          D
And the boys are at the bar,

              C
Yeah, they're mixing up their medicines.

        D   **C**   **G**
The girls are on their mobiles trying to get re - ception.

       D   **C**   **D**
And   Johnny's shadow's getting long but he keeps on singing,

                    C   **G**   **D**
His shadow's getting long but he keeps on singing.

Chorus 2
gradually
accelerating

       N.C.   **D**   **C**
But I was looking for you,

       D   **C**   **G**
Looking for you,

       D   **C**   **D**   **C** **G**
Looking for you in the city last night.

             D   **C**
And people so strange,

       D   **C**   **G**
People so strange,

       D   **C**   **D**   **C** **G** **D**
People just keep talking in the city at night.

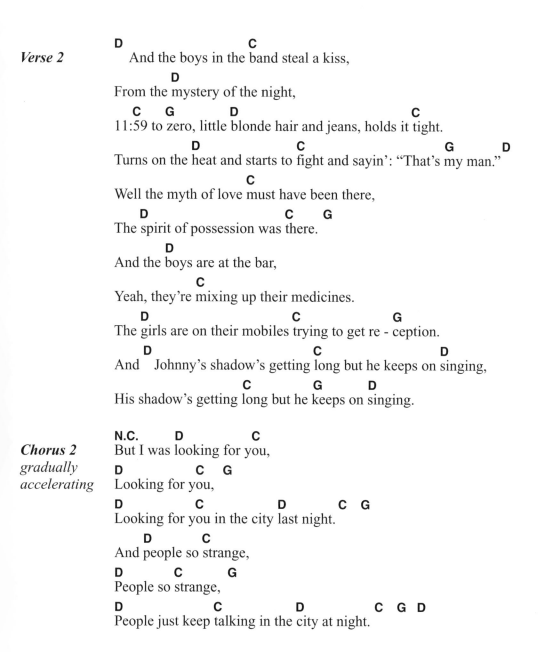

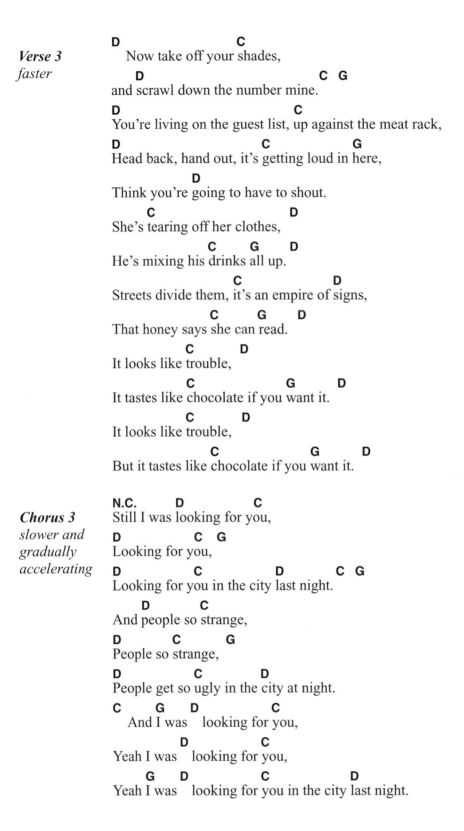

Verse 3
faster

    D   C
Now take off your shades,
        D   C G
and scrawl down the number mine.
D   C
You're living on the guest list, up against the meat rack,
D   C   G
Head back, hand out, it's getting loud in here,
                      D
Think you're going to have to shout.
     C   D
She's tearing off her clothes,
              C   G   D
He's mixing his drinks all up.
                  C   D
Streets divide them, it's an empire of signs,
              C   G   D
That honey says she can read.
          C   D
It looks like trouble,
          C   G   D
It tastes like chocolate if you want it.
          C   D
It looks like trouble,
              C   G   D
But it tastes like chocolate if you want it.

Chorus 3
slower and
gradually
accelerating

N.C.   D   C
Still I was looking for you,
D   C G
Looking for you,
D   C   D   C G
Looking for you in the city last night.
         D   C
And people so strange,
D   C   G
People so strange,
D   C   D
People get so ugly in the city at night.
C   G   D   C
  And I was   looking for you,
              D   C
Yeah I was   looking for you,
        G   D   C   D
Yeah I was   looking for you in the city last night.

cont.

```
C     G    D              C
  And I was   looking for you,
              D           C
Yeah I was   looking for you,
      G    D           C              D
Yeah I was   looking for you in the city last night.
```

Bridge
faster

```
C        G   D   C
  It was al - right,
              D     C
It was al - right,
        G   D    C
It was al - right,
              D     C
It was al - right,
        G       D      C
If you say my name,
              D      C G D  C D C  G
It's al - right.    Vocals ad lib.
```

Interlude

‖: D   C │ D C G │ D   C   │ D C G :‖ *Play 4 times*

Outro

```
              D  C    D  C    G D  C       D  C
  And yeah it's al - right, al - right,   al - right.
        G        D  C    D  C    G D  C       D  C
  And yeah it's al - right, al - right,   al - right.
        G        D  C    D  C    G D  C
  And yeah it's al - right, al - right,   al - right.
  D                   C
```

gradually
decelerating

```
Yeah, yeah, yeah, yeah.
  D          C
Ah, ah, ah, ah.
  D          C
Ah, ah, ah, ah.
  D
Well you know it's alright.
```

freely

```
     D
‖: It's alright. :‖  Repeat to fade
```

Jack And Diane

Words & Music by
John Cougar Mellencamp

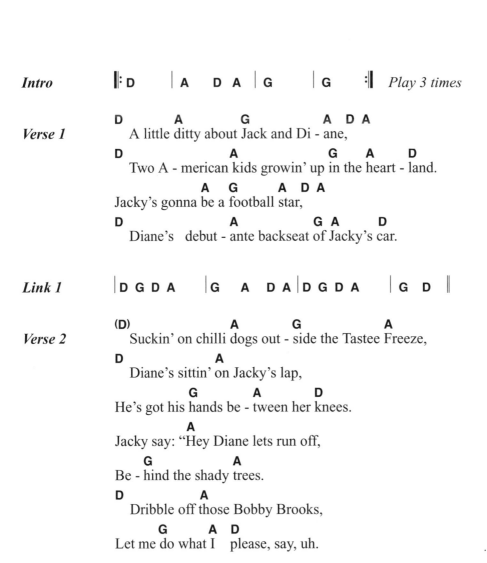

Capo 7th fret

Intro   ‖: D | A D A | G | G   :‖   *Play 3 times*

Verse 1

```
    D        A       G       A D A
    A little ditty about Jack and Di - ane,
    D           A          G    A    D
    Two A - merican kids growin' up in the heart - land.
               A  G     A D A
    Jacky's gonna be a football star,
    D          A        G A     D
    Diane's  debut - ante backseat of Jacky's car.
```

Link 1 | D G D A | G A D A | D G D A | G D ‖

Verse 2

```
    (D)              A       G           A
    Suckin' on chilli dogs out - side the Tastee Freeze,
    D          A
    Diane's sittin' on Jacky's lap,
             G       A       D
    He's got his hands be - tween her knees.
             A
    Jacky say: "Hey Diane lets run off,
    G            A
    Be - hind the shady trees.
    D          A
    Dribble off those Bobby Brooks,
    G        A D
    Let me do what I   please, say, uh.
```

Chorus 1

(D)   A   G   A
"Oh yeah life goes on,

D   A   G   A   D A
Long after the thrill of livin' is gone, say uh.

D   A   G   A
Oh yeah life goes on,

D   A   G   A D
Long after the thrill of livin' is gone."

They walk on.

Link 2

‖: D | A   D   A | G | G   :‖

Verse 3

D   A   G   A
Jack, he sits back, collects his thoughts for a moment,

D   A   G   A   D
Scratches his head and does his best James Dean.

          A   G   A D A
"Well man, me and Diane, we oughta run off to the ci - ty."

D   A   G   A   D
Diane says, "Baby, you ain't missin' no - thing."

And Jack, he say, ah:

Chorus 2

(D)   A   G   A
"Oh yeah life goes on,

D   A   G   A   D A
Long after the thrill of livin' is gone.

D   A
Oh yeah, well they say life goes on,   G   A

D   A   G   A D
Long after the thrill of livin' is gone."

(Harmony on bridge is implied by vocals, no chords played on guitar)

Bridge

D   G
Gonna let it rock,

            A
Let it roll,

D   G   C   G
Let the Bible Belt come and save my soul.

D   G   C   G
Hold on to sixteen as long as you can,

D   G
Changes come around real soon,

          A   D
Make us women and men.

Drums

Link 3

4

| D G D A | G   A   D A | D G D A | G   D |

Chorus 3

(D)   A   G   A
   Oh yeah life goes on,

D   A   G   A   D A
Long after the thrill of livin' is gone.

D   A   G   A
   Oh yeah, well they say life goes on,

D   A   G   A D
Long after the thrill of livin' is gone.

Outro

(D)   A   G   A
   A little ditty about Jack and Di - ane,

D   A   G   D
Two American kids doing the best they can.

‖: D   A | D A D A | G | G   :‖ *Repeat to fade*

Life Of Riley

Words & Music by
Ian Broudie

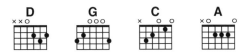

Tune guitar down by a tone

Intro | D G | C   G C G | D G | C   G C G |

| D | D | D | D ||

Verse 1
D
Lost in the milky way,
G
Smile at the empty sky
                    D
And wait for the moment
                                        G
A million chances may all collide.

Verse 2
D
I'll be the guiding light,
G
Swim to me through stars
                        D
That shine down and call
                                            G
To the sleeping world as they fall to earth.

Pre-chorus 1
        D
So here's your life,
            G
We'll find our way,
            D
We're sailing blind,
            G
But it's certain nothing's certain.

Chorus 1

D
I don't mind,

    G   D
I __ get the feeling you'll be fine.

    G   D
I __ still believe that in this world,

     G   A
We've got to find the time,

                     D   G |C   G C G|D G |C   G C G ‖
For the life of Riley.   From

Verse 3

            D
(From) cradles and sleepless nights,

      G
You breathe in life forever,

      D
And stare at the world

               G
From deep under eider - down.

Pre-chorus 2

       D
So here's your life,

      G
We'll find our way,

       D
We're sailing blind,

      G
But it's certain nothing's certain.

Chorus 2

D
I don't mind,

    G   D
I __ get the feeling you'll be fine.

    G   D
I __ still believe that in this world,

     G   A
We've got to find the time,

For the first time.

Chorus 3

D
I don't mind,

    G   D
I __ get the feeling you'll be fine.

    G   D
I __ still believe that in this world,

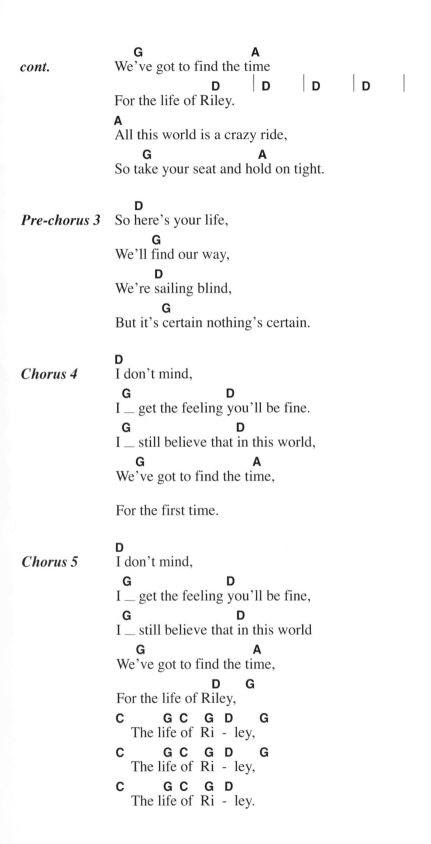

cont.

     G   A
We've got to find the time
         D | D | D | D |
For the life of Riley.

A
All this world is a crazy ride,

   G   A
So take your seat and hold on tight.

Pre-chorus 3

       D
So here's your life,

      G
We'll find our way,

      D
We're sailing blind,

      G
But it's certain nothing's certain.

Chorus 4

D
I don't mind,

 G   D
I — get the feeling you'll be fine.

 G   D
I — still believe that in this world,

  G   A
We've got to find the time,

For the first time.

Chorus 5

D
I don't mind,

 G   D
I — get the feeling you'll be fine,

 G   D
I — still believe that in this world

  G   A
We've got to find the time,

       D G
For the life of Riley,

C   G C G D G
 The life of Ri - ley,

C   G C G D G
 The life of Ri - ley,

C   G C G D
 The life of Ri - ley.

Mull Of Kintyre

Words & Music by
Paul McCartney & Denny Laine

D   **G**   **A**   **C**

Capo 7th fret

Intro | D | D | D | D   ‖

Chorus 1
D
Mull of Kintyre,
       G   D
Oh, mist rolling in from the sea,
           G
My desire is always to be here,
         D
Oh, Mull of Kintyre.

Verse 1
(D)
Far have I travelled and much have I seen,
G   D
Dark distant mountains with valleys of green.

Past painted deserts the sunset's on fire,
         G   A   D
As he carries me home to the Mull of Kin - tyre.

Chorus 2   As Chorus 1

Link | D | D |

Instrumental 1 | G | G | C | C |

        | G | G | C | C |

        | G | G | G | G   ‖

Verse 2

(G)
Sweep through the heather like deer in the glen,

C   G
Carry me back to the days I knew then.

Nights when we sang like a heavenly choir,

        C   D   G
Of the life and the times of the Mull of Kin - tyre.

Chorus 3

(G)
Mull of Kintyre,

      C   G
Oh, mist rolling in from the sea,

           C
My desire is always to be here,

 G
Oh, Mull of Kintyre.

Instrumental 2 | G | G | D | D |

                    | G | G | D | D   ‖

Verse 3

(D)
Smiles in the sunshine and tears in the rain,

G   D
Still take me back where my memories remain.

Flickering embers growing higher and higher,

        G   A   D
As they carry me back to the Mull of Kin - tyre.

Chorus 4   As Chorus 1

Chorus 5   As Chorus 3

Outro

      G   D
‖: Mull of Kintyre, oh, Mull of Kintyre. :‖ *Repeat to fade*

My Best Friend's Girl

Words & Music by
Ric Ocasek

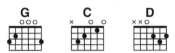

Tune guitar down by a tone

Intro   ‖: G | C D | G | C D :‖

Verse 1
　　　　　　　　　　　G
　　　You're always dancing down the street,
　　C　　　　　D　　　　　G　　C D
　　　With your suede blue eyes.
　　　　　　　　　G　　　　　　　　　C
　　And every new boy that you meet,
　　　　D　　　　　G　　　　　　C
　　He doesn't know the real surprise.
　　D　　　G
　　(Here she comes again.)
　　　　　　　　C　　　　　　　　　D
　　When she's dancing 'neath the starry sky,
　　G　　C　　　　　　　D　　　G
　　　Oo,　she'll make you flip.
　　　　　　　　　　　　　(Here she comes again.)
　　　　　　　　C　　　　　　　　　D
　　When she's dancing 'neath the starry sky,
　　G　　　C　　　　　　　D
　　　I kinda like the way she dips.

Chorus 1

```
           C   D                          C
Well she's my best friend's girl,
    D                         C       D
    She's my best friend's girl-irl,
                            |G      |C  D |G       |C  D  |
But she used to be mine.
```

Verse 2

```
                        G
You've got your nuclear boots,
    C          D      G   C
    And your drip dry glove.
    D            G
    Oo when you bite your lip,
    C             D      G           C
    It's some re - action to love, o-ove, o-ove.
D        G
(Here she comes again.)
                  C              D    G
When she's dancing 'neath the starry sky,
      C            D        G
Yeah,  I think you'll flip.
                        (Here she comes again.)
                  C              D       G
When she's dancing 'neath the starry sky,
                          (Here she comes again.)
            C          D              C
I kinda like the way, I like the way she dips.
```

Chorus 2

```
D                             C
    'Cause she's my best friend's girl,
D                           C
    Well she's my best friend's girl-irl,
D                    |G     |C  D     |G      |C  D  |
    And she used to be mine,       she's so  fine.
```

33

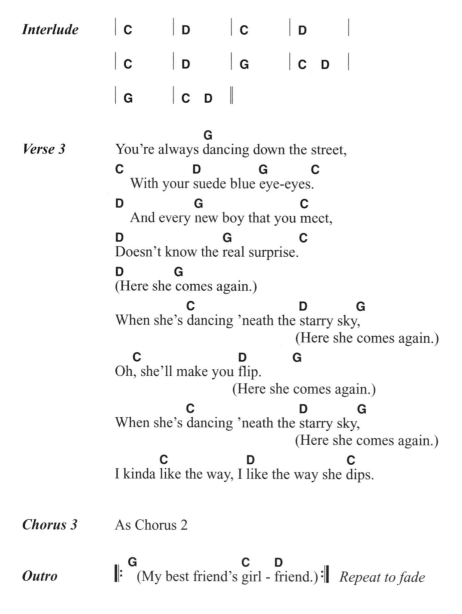

Interlude

| C | D | C | D |
| C | D | G | C D |
| G | C D ‖

Verse 3

                                    G
You're always dancing down the street,
  C   D   G   C
With your suede blue eye-eyes.
  D   G   C
And every new boy that you meet,
  D   G   C
Doesn't know the real surprise.
  D   G
(Here she comes again.)
           C   D   G
When she's dancing 'neath the starry sky,
                               (Here she comes again.)
    C   D   G
Oh, she'll make you flip.
                   (Here she comes again.)
           C   D   G
When she's dancing 'neath the starry sky,
                               (Here she comes again.)
      C   D   C
I kinda like the way, I like the way she dips.

Chorus 3   As Chorus 2

Outro   ‖: G   C   D
                 (My best friend's girl - friend.):‖ *Repeat to fade*

Praise You

Words & Music by
Norman Cook & Camille Yarborough

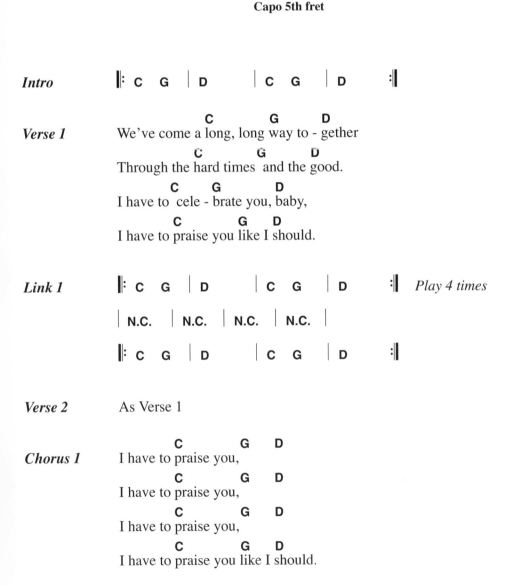

Capo 5th fret

Intro ‖: C G | D | C G | D   :‖

Verse 1
       C   G   D
We've come a long, long way to - gether
      C   G   D
Through the hard times and the good.
      C   G   D
I have to cele - brate you, baby,
      C   G D
I have to praise you like I should.

Link 1 ‖: C G | D | C G | D   :‖ *Play 4 times*

| N.C. | N.C. | N.C. | N.C. |

‖: C G | D | C G | D   :‖

Verse 2 As Verse 1

Chorus 1
      C   G D
I have to praise you,
      C   G D
I have to praise you,
      C   G   D
I have to praise you,
      C   G D
I have to praise you like I should.

Bridge 1

```
            A            D  G  │ A      D   G │ A      D   G │
I have to praise you,

     A    D    G A         D  G │ A     D   G │ A      D   G │
     I have to  praise you,

     A    D    G A        D   G
     I have to  praise you,
                 (Na   na   na   na,

     A        D    G
     Na   na  na    na.

     A        D    G
     Na   na  na    na.

     A        D    G
     Na   na  na    na.

     A        D    G
     Na   na  na    na.

     A        D    G
     Na   na  na    na.

     A        D    G
     Na   na  na    na.

     A        D    G │ C         G │ D            │
                 I have to   praise you.

     Na na na    na.)
```

Link 2

```
│ C  G │ D        │ C  G │ D        │ C  G │ D        ‖

│ N.C.  │ N.C.  │ N.C.  │ N.C.  │
```

Verse 3

```
                 C        G       D
We've come a long, long way to - gether
                 C       G      D
Through the hard times and the good.
             C    G        D
I have to  cele - brate you, baby,
             N.C.
I have to praise you like I should.
```

```
│ N.C.  │ N.C.  │ N.C.  │ N.C.  ‖
```

Chorus 2

        C   G   D
I have to praise you,

        C   G   D
I have to praise you,

        C   G   D
I have to praise you,

        C   G   D
I have to praise you,

        C   G   D
I have to praise you,

        C   G   D
I have to praise you,

        C   G   D
I have to praise you,

        C   G   D
I have to praise you like I should.

Bridge 2

        A   D G | A   D G |A   D G |
I have to praise you,

A   D   G A   D G |A   D G |A   D G |
   I have to praise you,

A   D   G
   I have to...

‖: A   D   G
   Praise you.
   (Na   na   na   na.

A   D   G
Na na na   na.

A   D   G
Na na na   na.

A   D   G   :‖ *Play 4 times*
          I have to...
Na na na   na.)

Ending

N.C.
Praise you.

Pain Killer (Summer Rain)

Words & Music by
Olly Knights & Gale Paridjanian

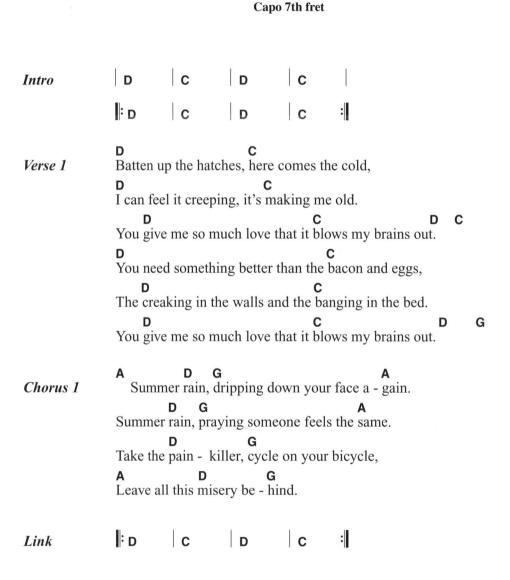

Capo 7th fret

Intro | D | C | D | C |

‖: D | C | D | C :‖

Verse 1

D   C
Batten up the hatches, here comes the cold,
D   C
I can feel it creeping, it's making me old.
      D   C   D C
You give me so much love that it blows my brains out.
D   C
You need something better than the bacon and eggs,
      D   C
The creaking in the walls and the banging in the bed.
      D   C   D   G
You give me so much love that it blows my brains out.

Chorus 1

A   D   G   A
   Summer rain, dripping down your face a - gain.
         D   G   A
Summer rain, praying someone feels the same.
         D   G
Take the pain - killer, cycle on your bicycle,
A   D   G
Leave all this misery be - hind.

Link ‖: D | C | D | C :‖

Verse 2

    D   **C**
My love, giving me head,

    D   **C**
Feeling very guilty, breaking the bread.

    D   **C**   **D** **C**
Losing my attention, I'm taking the world on.

      D   **C**
So batten up the hatches, here comes the cold

    D   **C**
I can feel it creeping, it's making me old

        D   **C**   **D**   **G**
You give me so much love that it blows my brains out.

Chorus 2   As Chorus 1

Bridge

    D   **C**
My love,

    D   **C**
My love,

    D   **C**
My love,

      D   **C**
Oh my love.

Chorus 3   As Chorus 1

Chorus 4   As Chorus 1

Outro

    A   **D**   **G**
Leave all this misery be - hind.

    A   **D**   **G**
Leave all this misery be - hind.

    A   **D**   **G**
Leave all this misery be - hind.

She Belongs To Me

Words & Music by
Bob Dylan

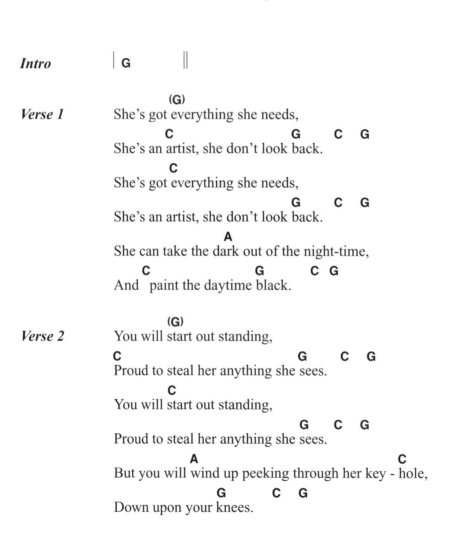

G   C   A

Capo 2nd fret

Intro | G ||

Verse 1
                    (G)
            She's got everything she needs,
                    C   **G   C   G**
            She's an artist, she don't look back.
                    C
            She's got everything she needs,
                                   G   C   G
            She's an artist, she don't look back.
                              A
            She can take the dark out of the night-time,
                    C   **G   C G**
            And   paint the daytime black.

Verse 2
                    (G)
            You will start out standing,
            C   **G   C   G**
            Proud to steal her anything she sees.
                          C
            You will start out standing,
                                   G   C   G
            Proud to steal her anything she sees.
                              A   **C**
            But you will wind up peeking through her key - hole,
                              G   C   G
            Down upon your knees.

Verse 3

(G)
She   never stumbles,

      C   G   C   G
She's got no place to fall.

      C
She never stumbles,

                G   C   G
She's got no place to fall.

        A
She's nobody's child,

      C   G   C   G
The Law can't touch her at all.

Link

G		C		G	C	G		C		C		

G	C	G		A		C		G	C	G	

Verse 4

(G)
She wears an Egyptian ring,

      C   G   C   G
It sparkles before she speaks.

        C
She wears an Egyptian ring,

           G   C   G
It sparkles before she speaks.

        A
She's a hypnotist collector,

      C   G   C   G
You are a walking an - tique.

Verse 5

(G)
Bow down to her on Sunday,

      C   G   C   G
Sa - lute her when her birthday comes.

      C
Bow down to her on Sunday,

                G   C   G
Salute her when her birthday comes.

          A
For Hallow - een buy her a trumpet,

      C   G   C   G
And for Christmas, get her a drum.

Coda

‖: G | C | G C | G :‖ *Repeat to fade*

Rocks

Words & Music by
Bobby Gillespie, Robert Young & Andrew Innes

D   C   G   A

Capo 7th fret

Intro | D | C   G | D | C   G |
         | D | C   G | D | C   G ‖

Verse 1
D
Deal - ers keep dealin', thieves keep thievin',
C   G   D
Whores keep   whorin', junkies keep scorin'.

Trade is on the meat rack, strip joints full of hunch-backs,
C   G   D
Bitches keep   bitchin', clap just keeps itchin'.

Bridge 1
A
Ain't no use in prayin',
C   D | D |
That's the way it's stayin' baby.
A
Johnny ain't so crazy,
C   G
He's always got a line for the ladies,

Yeah, yeah, yeah.

Chorus 1
          D   C
Get __ your rocks off, get your rocks off honey,
          G
Shake __ it now now, get 'em off down town.
          D   C
Get __ your rocks off, get your rocks off honey,
          G
Shake __ it now now, get 'em off down town.

Link 1   ‖: D | C G | D | C G :‖

                            D

Verse 2   Creeps ___ keep crawlin', drunks keep fallin',

              C   G   D

Teasers keep   teasin', Holy Joes are preachin'.

Cops keep bustin', hustlers keep hustlin',

     C   G   D

Death keeps a-knockin', souls are up for auction.

           A

Bridge 2 Ain't no use in prayin',

          C   D | D |

That's the way it's stayin' baby.

          A

Johnny ain't so crazy,

          C   G

He's always got a line for the ladies,

Yeah, yeah, yeah.

            D   C

Chorus 2 Get ___ your rocks off, get your rocks off honey,

            G

Shake ___ it now now, get 'em off down town.

            D   C

Get ___ your rocks off, get your rocks off honey,

            G

Shake ___ it now now, get 'em off down town.

Link 2   ‖: D | C G | D | C G :‖

Bridge 3

    A
Ain't no use in prayin',

    C   **D** | **D** |
That's the way it's stayin' baby.

    A
Johnny ain't so crazy,

    C   **G**
He's always got a line for the ladies,

Yeah, yeah, yeah.

Chorus 3

          D   **C**
Get ___ your rocks off, get your rocks off honey,

        G
Shake ___ it now now, get 'em off down town.

          D   **C**
Get ___ your rocks off, get your rocks off honey,

        G
Shake ___ it now now, get 'em off down town.

Chorus 4

          D   **C**
Get ___ your rocks off, get your rocks off honey,

        G
Shake ___ it now now, get 'em off down town.

                            C
Get ___ your rocks off, get your rocks off honey,

        G
Shake ___ it now now, get 'em off down town.

Outro

          D   **C**
‖: Get ___ your rocks off, get your rocks off honey,

    G
Get ___ your rocks off, get your rocks off honey. :‖ *Repeat to fade*

Tiger Feet

Words & Music by
Mike Chapman & Nicky Chinn

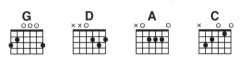

Capo 9th fret

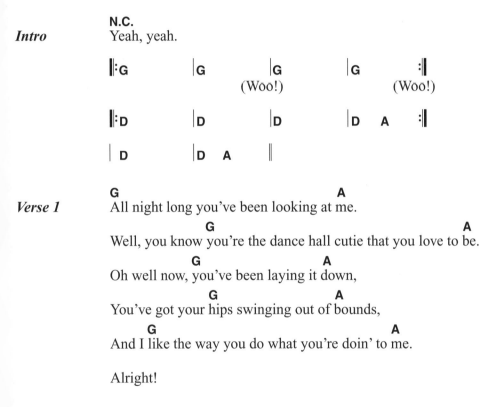

Intro

N.C.
Yeah, yeah.

```
‖: G        | G          | G          | G          :‖
              (Woo!)                    (Woo!)

‖: D        | D          | D          | D    A     :‖

 | D        | D    A     ‖
```

Verse 1

    G   **A**
All night long you've been looking at me.

              G   **A**
Well, you know you're the dance hall cutie that you love to be.

            G   **A**
Oh well now, you've been laying it down,

            G   **A**
You've got your hips swinging out of bounds,

      G   **A**
And I like the way you do what you're doin' to me.

Alright!

                     D
Chorus 1   That's right, that's right, that's right, that's right
                        C   **G** **D**
                 I really love your tiger light.

                 That's neat, that's neat, that's neat, that's neat,
                        C   **G** **D**
                 I really love your tiger feet.
                        C   **G** **D**
                 I really love your tiger feet.
                 A   **C**   **D**
                    Your tiger feet,
                 A   **C**   **D**
                    Your tiger feet,
                 A   **C**   **D**
                    Your tiger feet.
                 A
                 Alright!

Guitar solo 1   ‖:**D** |**D** |**D** |**D**   **A**   :‖

                  | **D** |**D**   **A**   ‖

                        G   **A**
Verse 2   Well, flash your warning lights just as long as you like.
                        G   **A**
                 I know you're aching to be making me to - night.
                      G   **A**
                 I've got a feeling in my knees,
                      G   **A**
                 A feeling only you can please,
                          G   **A**
                 There ain't no way I'm gonna let you outta my sight.

                 Alright!

Chorus 2   As Chorus 1

46

Guitar solo 2   As Guitar Solo 1

Bridge 1   ‖: D | D | D | D   C   :‖   *Play 4 times*

        D
That's right, (that's right), that's right, (that's right),
       C   D
I really love your tiger light.

That's neat, (that's neat), that's neat, (that's neat),
       C   D
I really love your tiger feet.
       C   D
I really love your tigcr fcct.

                         G   A
Verse 3   Well, alright now, you've been laying it down,
                     G   A
You've got your hips swinging out of bounds,
      G   A
And I like the way you do what you're doin' to me.

Alright!

Chorus 3   As Chorus 1

     D
Outro   ‖: That's right, that's right, that's right, that's right,

That's right, that's right, that's right, that's right.
G
That's néat, that's neat, that's neat, that's neat.
      D   A
I really love, I really love, I really love, I really love,
        G   D   A
I really love your tiger feet.   :‖   *Repeat to fade*

2/10(173071)   3 4 5 6 7 8 9

Relative Tuning

The guitar can be tuned with the aid of pitch pipes or dedicated electronic guitar tuners which are available through your local music dealer. If you do not have a tuning device, you can use relative tuning. Estimate the pitch of the 6th string as near as possible to E or at least a comfortable pitch (not too high, as you might break other strings in tuning up). Then, while checking the various positions on the diagram, place a finger from your left hand on the:

5th fret of the E or 6th string and **tune the open A** (or 5th string) to the note (A)

5th fret of the A or 5th string and **tune the open D** (or 4th string) to the note (D)

5th fret of the D or 4th string and **tune the open G** (or 3rd string) to the note (G)

4th fret of the G or 3rd string and **tune the open B** (or 2nd string) to the note (B)

5th fret of the B or 2nd string and **tune the open E** (or 1st string) to the note (E)

E A D G B E
or or or or or or
6th 5th 4th 3rd 2nd 1st

Head

Nut

1st Fret

2nd Fret

3rd Fret

4th Fret

5th Fret

Reading Chord Boxes

Chord boxes are diagrams of the guitar neck viewed head upwards, face on as illustrated. The top horizontal line is the nut, unless a higher fret number is indicated, the others are the frets.

The vertical lines are the strings, starting from E (or 6th) on the left to E (or 1st) on the right.

The black dots indicate where to place your fingers.

Strings marked with an O are played open, not fretted.
Strings marked with an X should not be played.

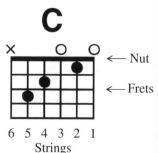

C

← Nut

← Frets

6 5 4 3 2 1
Strings